100 Years of Farming

in and around the Clwydian Range

Lorna Jenner

Copyright © 2009 **Alyn Books** Ltd, The Nook, Pentre Road, Cilcain, Mold, Flintshire CH7 5PD.

ISBN 978-0-9559625-5-4

Modern photography: Jo Danson, Lorna Jenner, Jackie Lewis, Carl Rogers, Phil Parsons
Printed by: Ashford Press

With special thanks to all the farmers and their families who have shared memories and photographs with me, to those who have allowed us to photograph them as they worked, to the Clwydian Range AONB, and to Ruthin and Mold Livestock markets for making us so welcome.

Space has limited what material could be included. I apologise to those whose stories and photographs have not been used but all helped to set the scene and give me the flavour of local farming in years gone by.

Front cover image:Robert Jones at the plough and Edward Jones leading the horses at Kinsale, Greenfield, October 1972
Courtesy of Vicky Jones, © St Fagans: National History Museum

British Library Cataloguing-in-publication data.

A catalogue is available for this book from the British Library.

Whilst every effort has been made to ensure that the information in this book is correct, the author or the publisher can accept no responsibility for errors.

To farmers in and around the Clwydian Range

Grant-aided by the AONB Sustainable Development Fund

Foreword

It is both a privilege and pleasure to me to have been asked to write a foreword to this photographic celebration of farming in the Clwydian Range over the last century.

Possibly I was asked because it was thought that I am one of the last survivors over that period and, indeed, I have been associated with the Golden Grove Estate at the northern end of the Area of Outstanding Natural Beauty since before the Second World War.

The changes in that time have been astonishing. The smallholdings farmed by miners working down the pit at Point of Ayr have gone, together with the mine itself. The land has been amalgamated into bigger units and the cottages sold. The livestock kept and the crops grown have altered beyond belief. The Dairy Shorthorns kept in my childhood have been replaced, first by Friesians, and later by Holsteins. The time when every farmer kept cows has gone; now only one dairy farm remains, keeping far more cows than were then on the whole estate. The Herefords that were used for beef crosses have been replaced by Charollais and Limousin. Even the sheep flocks of Welsh ewes have been replaced by halfbreds and mules, with Texel rams instead of Suffolks. Pigs and poultry have vanished. Crops too have changed, with silage and then haylage largely replacing hay, while the small plots of swedes, mangolds and potatoes have gone. Barley has replaced oats as the main cereal crop but grass predominates. Mechanisation is, of course, the most visible change so that now, in employment terms, agriculture is now a bit player.

However the farming families still remain and provide an essential base to life in the Clwydian Range. They are the last bastion of the language of heaven and are the guardians of the Range in its seasonal coats. They have changed through the years, while retaining so much continuity. It is a key responsibility of the Joint Advisory Committee of the Area of Outstanding Beauty, of which I have been a member for so many years, to help and support them in this. Long may they continue.

Nigel Steele Mortimer
Golden Grove

Bryniau Clwyd
Clwydian Range

Ardal o Harddwch Naturiol Eithriadol
Area of Outstanding Natural Beauty

Contents

Chapter 1

Setting the scene

This book is a celebration of the rich farming heritage on and around the Clwydian Range. It is not meant to be a history of farming as I do not have a farming background and would not presume to try and write a serious account. What I have tried to do, through the use of photographs and anecdotes, is to catch the essence of farming and to document some of the changes that have taken place over the past century. Numerous farmers have helped me putting the book together, some bringing along old photographs and sharing their memories, others patiently explaining farming practices and showing me round their farms. The old photographs paint an evocative picture of the earlier days of farming and they are supplemented by modern photographs, taken on local farms, at shows and at livestock markets.

The photographs capture such things as the frenetic activity of haymaking or harvesting and the well-earned tea break in the fields; the shepherd's pride in a well-trained sheepdog or a prize winning ram; the atmosphere of the livestock market; the concentration of the ploughman and his fondness for his horses, the skilled work of the blacksmith and wheelwright, and the backbreaking work of the scythesman or potato picker.

Farming has changed enormously over the last hundred years. Older farmers recall milking and shearing by hand, using steam-driven threshing machines, building haystacks, ploughing with horses and the purchase of their first tractors. In contrast, modern farms are highly mechanized and fewer hands are needed to run them as tractors, harvestors and other machinery have grown in size, cost and sophistication. Farms have got bigger and there are far fewer than there once were.

Left: *Corn binder at Maes-y-Groes, Cilcain, in the 1930s* (courtesy of the Worthington family)

Right: *Paul and Gaynor Roberts with Suffolk sheep, 1959, Ty Mawr, Tremeirchion* (courtesy of Mark Roberts)

Ruthin Farmers Auction

Tea break, or 'bagging', Plas yn Cwm, Waen
(courtesy of Margaret Stanyer)

Turning hay at Ty Gwyn, Tremeirchion, 1950s
(courtesy of Clare Evans)

Firwood Farm, 1940s

At the turn of the 20th century there were more farms on the Clwydian Range and most were much smaller. Traditionally each small farm was mixed, keeping livestock and growing a variety of crops. The following extract from a letter by Minnie Peake of Firwood Farm, Nannerch, to her brother in America, illustrates the typical mix of crop and animal husbandry:

'Our corn looks middling, hay is pretty fair, turnips and potatoes are alright. We are milking 6 cows, 2 of them are heifers and have 8 weaning calves, 6 horses and sheep – I cannot give you the count but think so far we have done well. At present we only have 2 sows but we have just sold 9 pigs and one is weaning tonight. We don't keep ducks now, they want running after and our legs are not so young as they used to be. We do not get many eggs for we have not many hens, about 30 and we used to have nearly 100. We churn twice a week and get 30-35lbs of butter. I think we shall have a fair amount of fruit this year. Gooseberries are very fine & blackcurrants.'

Firwood Farm, July 4th, 1910

Pottinger forager, Maes-y-Groes Bella, Cilcain

Modern farms are generally larger and more specialized but with a smaller workforce. For example, in the past, almost every farm kept at least one or two milking cows, whereas, nowadays there are only a handful of dairy farms in the whole of the Clwydian Range.

Today's farmers are not battling with the elements to quite the same extent, although good periods of warm weather and sufficient rain are still essential, and heavy winter snow can still cause problems. The change from hay to silage has reduced the need for a long spell of fine weather during haymaking, and the introduction of combine harvesters that cut and thresh the corn in one operation has revolutionised harvesting. Ploughing inside a warm heated tractor with good suspension is very different from working with horses or on open topped early tractors. A nippy quad bike saves the feet when rounding up sheep!

But, despite the benefits that improved technology has brought, modern farmers face other challenges. They are weighed down with paperwork and regulations. The frequently changing payment schemes cause headaches for all and the modern farmer needs to be a computer wizard, skilled at interpreting forms, with a flexible and sharp business head. However, although farming methods have changed so much over the past century, the deep affinity between Clwydian farmers and the landscape in which they live and work remains unchanged.

Above: *Bracken control*
(courtesy of the Clwydian Range AONB)

Right: Fencing to protect a laid
hedge, Maes-y-Groes, Cilcain

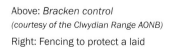

Chapter 2

Horse power

Farming in this area remained largely dependent on horse power for heavy work until after the Second World War and some farms continued to use horses until well into the 1950s. Shire horses were used to pull ploughs and for other heavy work with smaller Welsh cobs used for all other work. A prize shire stallion was a valuable possession and the old photographs show that the horses were obviously the pride and joy of their owners.

> 'Walter Langford, the landlord at the White Horse, Cilcain, kept shire stallions to sire the local farm horses. One particular stallion, Robin Hood VII, was renowned as it served 390 mares in a season and was given a bottle of Guinness after each one!'
>
> Vincent Vaughan

Smaller Welsh cobs were used for all other work. The cobs were versatile animals as they were strong and willing. They would work on the farm 6 days a week, pulling carts and lighter machinery, and then be harnessed to the trap to take the family to church on Sundays. They were also good riding horses.

> 'A good Welsh cob was the family motor car of its day!'
>
> John Rees

Top right: *Pistyll Farm, Bodfari*
(courtesy of Fiona Evans)

Right: *Maes-y-Groes, Cilcain, 1930s*
(courtesy of the Worthington family)

Left: *Bob and Ted Jones ploughing at Kinsale, Greenfield, October 1972.*
Courtesy of Vicky Jones, © St Fagans: National History Museum

Above: *Huw Jones with his shire stallion outside Hope and Anchor pub, Denbigh, 1920s*
(courtesy of Dilys Jones)
Above left: *Maes-y-Groes, Cilcain (courtesy of the Worthington family)*
Below left: *Aberduna Farm, Maeshafn (courtesy of Roger Jones)*
Below right: *Ffordd Hir, Pantymwyn (courtesy of the Davies family)*

Glyn, Matti and Bob Edwards, Fron Farm Hendre, with their team of young mares, Queen and Jewel, at the Flintshire Ploughing Match in the 1950s. Bob was the Welsh National Horse Ploughing Champion in 1994 (courtesy of Bob Edwards)

Ioan Davies, Pistyll Farm, Nercwys (courtesy of Ray Davies)

Ivor Hughes, Bryn Farm, Tremeirchion (courtesy of Delyth Potts)

'As a lad I used the hayrake pulled by a horse to gather the dry hay into rows. My sister used to help by pulling off any hay that became tangled in the machinery with a long fork. Our hayrake was later adapted so it could be pulled by a tractor.'

John James Parry,
Maes y Garnedd Farm, Tafarn-y-Gelyn

Horse and trap from Mount Pleasant Dairy, Gwernaffield (courtesy of the Shawcross family)

Planting potatoes, Ysceifiog (courtesy of Hazel Formby)

Grinding root crops for fodder using a horse whim, Henfaes Farm, Nannerch, circa 1900
(courtesy of the Morris family)

Mowing at Rhual, Gwernaffield (courtesy of Major Heaton)

18

Pistyll Farm, Bodfari (courtesy of Fiona Evans)

Willie Woodward, Tafarn-y-Gelyn, 1936 (courtesy of Anne Woodward)

Hay cart, Llanarmon-yn-Iâl (courtesy of Olwen Roberts)

Tecwyn Morris of Henfaes Farm, Nannerch, with his ploughing trophies. He was British Horse Ploughing Champion in 1972 and 1973
(courtesy of the Morris family)

Ploughing demonstration, Kinsale, October 1972 by champion ploughmen, Ted Jones of Plas Tirion Farm, Whitford and his brother Bob, of Kinsale Hall, Holywell.
Courtesy of Vicky Jones, © St Fagans: National History Museum

'Unig uchelgais llanc o'r wlad
Yw torri cŵys fel cŵys ei Dad.'
Cynan

'The sole ambition of a country lad
Is to plough a furrow as well as his dad.'
Anon (a translation from the Welsh)

Ploughing with horses was a highly skilled job, and ploughmen took great pride in ploughing a straight furrow. Since the late 1800s, many counties have held annual ploughing matches, when local farmers competed to turn the grassland during the winter months with their horse drawn ploughs. The competitions were widened to include tractor classes from the 1950s and the introduction of motor vehicles, enabled ploughmen to travel further to compete. A British Ploughing Competition was established in 1951 and a Welsh National competition was established in1958. This area produced many fine ploughmen who have won the national competitions on many occasions.

Modern tractors have completely taken over the work of horses but a few enthusiasts still carry on the tradition of horse ploughing, regularly competing and demonstrating at Agricultural Shows. It is still a magnificent sight that always draws admiring crowds.

Right: *Ploughing at Aelwyd Uchaf (courtesy of Evelyn Lloyd Davies)*
Below: *Horse ploughing at Caerwys 2010*

The blacksmith and wheelwright

Nowadays, specialist engineers are needed to repair some of the sophisticated, modern farm machinery but, in the early 20th century, farmers relied on the blacksmith and wheelwright.

The blacksmith was an important figure in every village, essential not only for shoeing the farm horses but also for repairing farm machinery and sharpening tools. Work declined following the gradual replacement of working horses by tractors and most village smithies had closed by the mid 20th century.

However, the smithy at Nercwys is still thriving and has been run by the same family for at least five generations. As the work shoeing farm horses declined, the increasing popularity of horse-riding for pleasure brought new work. The present farrier travels far and wide, working with racehorses and shoeing horses for international competitions.

The wheelwright was also important for local farmers, making and repairing wheels for the horse drawn carts and other machinery. The blacksmith made the metal rims for the wheels at his forge and they were heated and fitted round the wooden wheels by the wheelwright. When the first tractors arrived on the farms, a skilled wheelwright was invaluable, converting the shafts on the ploughs and carts so that they could be pulled by a tractor.

The Hughes brothers working at Tremeirchion smithy, 1931. They were blacksmiths here for over 50 years. (courtesy of Flintshire Record Office)

Above: *Ted Hughes at work in Nercwys smithy*
Below: *Outside Nercwys smithy*
(courtesy of Ray Davies)

Left: *Farrier Ian Hughes in Nercwys smithy, 2010*
(courtesy of Glyn Hughes)

Bill Jones, the last blacksmith at Northop smithy in the 1970s
(courtesy of Dorothy Jones)

Adam Woodward, wheelwright, joiner and undertaker,
working with his assistant at Tafarn-y-Gelyn, circa 1950
(courtesy of Anne Woodward)

Chapter 3

Many hands

At the beginning of the 20th century, little machinery was available and most farm work was done by hand, from digging ditches and felling trees to potato planting and picking, sowing seed and weeding.

Hay and cereals were often cut by hand with scythes. A team of men would cut each field, the leading scythesman setting off, making three or four cuts, before the next man set off, so that a staggered team of men were swinging scythes across the field. At the end of each run, they would walk back to sharpen their scythes before starting on the next section. Gradually, the farms acquired horse-drawn cutting machines, but scythes continued to be used for field corners and to open a swathe at the edge of a field so that the machines could start cutting without going through standing corn.

Top: *Ty Mawr, Tremeirchion*
(courtesy of Mark Roberts)
Right: *Shooting rabbits at Greenbank, Tremeirchion (courtesy of Gwynfa Derosa)*
Far right: *Digging ditches at Henblas, Tremeirchion (courtesy of Linda Roberts)*

Left: *Cutting with scythe, Pen-y-Mynydd, Nannerch*
(courtesy of Betty Kent)

27

Fields were enclosed by hedges and dry stonewalls, built from local stone. Hedgelaying, to encourage a dense, stock-proof hedge, and walling were particularly skilled tasks. Post and wire fencing, which require less maintenance, have replaced these traditional boundaries in many areas, but in the Clwydian Range, stone walls still snake across the hillsides and most fields are still bounded by thick hedgerows, adding to the special character of the landscape. There are still skilled hedgelayers and wallers working locally and the skills can be learnt through courses run by the Clwydian Range AONB.

Volunteers learning walling from Arwel Huws on the Clwydian Range
(courtesy of the Clwydian Range AONB)

Idris Blackwell hedgelaying in Cilcain (courtesy of Dennis Kemp)

Volunteers learning hedgelaying on the Clwydian Range
(courtesy of the Clwydian Range AONB)

Tom Davies in a hedgelaying competition in the early 1980s
(courtesy of Dilys Jones)

Bringing in the harvest

Haymaking and harvesting required many hands. Adjoining farms pooled their workforce and also employed itinerant workers and casual labour. School attendance was low as many boys took time off to help too.

Hay was usually cut in June and was always a race against the weather. Once cut, the hay was left to dry in the fields for several days. During this time it was turned once, either with pikels (pitchforks) or with a horse-drawn hay tedder, before being gathered into piles with a hayrake then loaded onto a cart and taken to where it was to be stored and built up into a haystack with pitchforks. The finished stack was often thatched to protect the hay from rain. Alternatively the loose hay was piled into a barn for storage.

Above: *Haymaking at Greenbank Farm, Tremeirchion*
(courtesy of Gwynfa Derosa)

Above right: *Raking hay*
(courtesy of Meinir Shiel)

Right: *Cutting the hay at Greenbank Farm, Tremeirchion*
(courtesy of Gwynfa Derosa)

Enjoying a break during haymaking, Erw Goed, Nercwys
(courtesy of Meinir Shiel)

Pantygraig, Pantymwyn (courtesy of the Davies family)

The Old Vicarage, Llanarmon-yn-Iâl (courtesy Mair Lloyd)

The Stoddart family, Llanarmon-yn-Iâl (courtesy of Kathleen Jones)

'My father wouldn't let us use a hay tedder to turn the hay as he said it knocked off the seed heads, reducing the quality. It was hard work turning it all by hand with pikels but our cattle always fattened up very well on our hand-turned hay!'

Bob Edwards, Fron Farm, Hendre

'Haymaking in the 1930s was a busy time, needing lots of extra hands, especially for piling the hay into a big haycock with pitchforks. All the family helped but also casual workers, mainly out-of-work colliers. They were strong and willing but were used to working underground with picks and shovels and weren't skilled wielding a pitchfork – you needed to stand well clear!'

Thos Roberts , Hendre Isa farm, Nercwys

Maes-y-Groes, Cilcain
(courtesy of the Worthington family)

Pistyll Farm, Bodfari (courtesy of Fiona Evans)

Bryn Farm, Tremeirchion (courtesy of Delyth Potts)

In the fields at Llanarmon-yn-Iâl
(courtesy of Olwen Roberts)

Steam threshing at Llanelidan, 1910 (courtesy of Denbighshire Record Office)

Stooking sheaves of corn, Ty Ucha, Waen
(courtesy of Margaret Stanyer)

Corn binder at Henfaes, Nannerch (courtesy of the Morris family)

The ripe corn was harvested in late August or September, initially by hand but later using horse-drawn corn binders that cut the corn and dropped it onto a mechanical platform. Rollers carried the cut corn up to a knotter machine that gathered the corn into bundles and tied them before throwing out the sheaves. Four or five sheaves were stacked into a stook and left to dry in the field. When the sheaves were dry enough to store they were pitched onto horse drawn-wagons and either piled outdoors to form a big stack, which was thatched with rushes for protection from the elements, or taken to a barn for storage.

In October the mobile threshing machine, powered by a steam engine, would go from farm to farm to separate the corn from the stalks and chaff. Threshing was a big event as at least 10 men were needed. It took all day and the farmer's wife always laid on a great spread of food to sustain the hungry workers. The sheaves of corn were thrown up to a man on top of the threshing machine who fed them into the spinning threshing drum. The corn poured out of the chutes into sacks while straw and chaff came out separately.

'As you neared the bottom of the rick, lots of rats would always run out. We tied string round the bottom of our trousers to stop the rats running up! I remember helping threshing in the stackyard at Ty Ucha where the rats used to run to hide in a granite wall at the back of the stackyard. My uncle, Si Langford, was a hard man. He put his hand into a hole in the wall, pulled out a rat and either squeezed it to death with his hands or banged it on the head – reputedly he killed 81 that day!'

Vincent Vaughan, Cilcain

Threshing machine and steam engine, Aelwyd Uchaf, Tremeirchion (courtesy of Evelyn Lloyd Davies)

Harvesting corn at Maes-y-Groes, Cilcain in the 1930s
(courtesy of the Worthington family)

Building the stack

Threshing the corn

During the Second World War when the male work-force was seriously depleted, many 'Land Girls', young women who had joined the Women's Land Army, worked on local farms. Many had come from cities, particularly Liverpool, but took to the rural life and some ended up marrying local farmers and settling in the area.

Land girl working a baling machine (courtesy of Noel Jones)

Land girl, Margaret Benjamin working at Ty Ucha, Waen. She stayed on after the war and married the farmer's son, Patrick Stanyer
(courtesy of Margaret Stanyer neé Benjamin)

Land girls at Gwasaney, near Mold, who stayed at the hostel at Rhyd Alyn
(courtesy of Olwen Jones)

Prisoners of War potatato picking at Maes Mynan Farm, Afonwen
(courtesy of Dilys Jones)

Later in the war, many Prisoners of War were also sent to work on local farms to help the labour shortage. Most were housed in camps and were taken by lorry to different farms on a daily basis, depending on the work that was needed. A few were billeted on farms. Some POWs continued to work for several years after the war as not all could be repatriated immediately and there was still an acute labour shortage. Some were offered freedom and paid work if they agreed to stay on for an additional year. Most eventually returned home but a few settled locally.

'The first POWs we got were the Italians. They were marvellous – noisy and squabbling amongst themselves but always cheerful, and they worked really hard. We'd never met anyone from foreign parts until then.'

Elvet Pierce, Gelli Farm, Nannerch

'I had been a paratrooper in the German army fighting on the left bank of the Rhine. In September 1944, I was badly wounded and captured. When I had recovered in hospital, I was taken to the UK and spent time at various camps, working mainly on farms and then at Bees Nurseries at Sealand.

In 1947, I was sent to live and work at Pen Llan Farm, Cilcain. I got on very well with the farmer, who was only a few years older than me and made me very welcome. An officer from the War Agricultural Committee asked if I would stay on for another year of farm work, working as a free man and receiving a wage. I accepted when I realized that I was not due to be repatriated for some time.

In December 1948 I went home briefly to see my family, but soon returned to marry my sweetheart, who lived on a neighbouring farm. I have stayed in the area since then, mainly working on farms and in forestry.'

Frank Bluhm, Cilcain

Frank Bluhm at Pen Llan, Cilcain, 1952 (courtesy of Frank Bluhm)

Chapter 4

Mechanisation

Tractors were first used on some British farms during the First World War but were not widespread for many years. By the 1930s, only one in fifteen British farms had use of a tractor, and this was probably even lower in north east Wales, where many local farms remained dependent on horse and manpower until the 1940s or 50s.

The Second World War had a huge impact on farming, greatly speeding up the rate of mechanization and stimulating the development of more intensive, scientific methods of farming. Prior to the war, over a fifth of the population was employed in agriculture but Britain still imported most of its food, as farming methods were traditional and not highly efficient. German blockades and U boats, who were sinking thousands of tonnes of shipping, cut off the supply of imports, so there was a massive drive to increase production in order to feed the population.

Each district established a War Agricultural Executive Committee to coordinate activities of local farmers to maximize production. They had tractors and other machinery at their disposal, could organize mobile groups of farm workers and had powers to direct what could be grown and to inspect farms. Farmers were encouraged to plant additional cereals or root crops, so large areas of grassland were ploughed for the first time. As a result, food production almost doubled in five years.

Above right: *Sam Evans and Adam Woodward mowing at Llanferres in the 1950s*
(courtesy of Anne Woodward)

Left: *Combining at Ty Ucha, Waen, around 1950*
(courtesy of Margaret Stanyer)

Right: *Testing a Jones baler at Henllan*
(courtesy of Noel Jones)

Ken Lewis and his team threshing at Ty Mawr Farm, Cilcain, during the war. The original sketch is thought to have been drawn by Doris Ward, an evacuee from Liverpool, redrawn by Tim Johnson.

Ken and Geoff Lewis threshing, 1950s
(courtesy of Ken Lewis)

'During the war, there was a great shortage of threshing contractors as far more crops were being grown. In 1940, my brother and I bought a small American Case Model R tractor and leased a threshing machine from the 'War Ag'. We went from farm to farm, mainly in the Cilcain area. More machinery was being sent by ship from America through the Lend-lease scheme. In 1942, we bought a larger Case LA tractor and leased another that had been shipped to Liverpool on the SS Montevideo. They were the only Case tractors in North Wales and were really good machines. By the end of the war, we were running three threshing outfits across a wide area.'

Ken Lewis, Cyfnant Uchaf, Llanarmon-yn-Iâl

In the early days a skilled ploughman and horses could beat the new tractors but as technology improved and tractor drivers increased in skill, the tractors soon outstripped the horses. An experienced ploughman could turn one acre per day with a good team of horses but a modern tractor can plough up to 20 acres per day! Tractors rapidly evolved, becoming more powerful and able to pull an increasing number of farm machines. Vans, landrovers and trailers replaced horse-drawn wagons and carts, gradually bringing the era of horse power to an end.

'In 1943 we got our first tractor, a Fordson Bach, that we shared with a neighbouring farm. At first we just used it for ploughing as most of our farm implements had shafts for attaching to our horses and needed to be converted for the tractor. Your arms really ached after driving the tractor – it had metal wheels and no suspension or power steering – but we youngsters thought it was wonderful!

Idris Jones, Treuddyn

Ferguson tractors on the North Wales Agricultural Engineers stand at the Royal Welsh Show, at Abergele in the 1950s
(courtesy of Bryn Jones)

'At the annual Cilcain Ploughing match of 1950 the wet clay soil caused all sorts of problems for the horses and ploughs. The Ferguson tractor company demonstrated their new tractor with a hydraulic plough. The farmers were so impressed with the new machinery that 11 new tractors were ordered that day!'

Harry Williams, Fforest Farm, Cilcain

Demonstration of a Ferguson Tractor pulling a cultivator
(courtesy of Bryn Jones)

Glynne and David Jones with traction engine, circa 1930s
(courtesy of Noel Jones)

Moving bales was far easier than mounds of loose straw
(courtesy of Idris Jones)

As the war progressed there was a great shortage of spare parts and materials. No new machinery was built because all materials were needed for the war effort. Make do and mend became as much the rule on the farm as it was in the home - old wheels, pieces of scrap metal, nuts and bolts and screws were all kept and re-used. Farmers became adept at adapting and making their own equipment. This spirit led to the development locally of one of Britain's most famous agricultural companies, Jones Balers.

The Jones brothers, Glynne and David, had worked as farm labourers, after being evicted from their farm during the 1920s farming depression. Eventually, they bought steam-powered machinery and went from farm to farm doing heavy work such as pulling up stumps and threshing. Harvesting was still very labour intensive and two of the most time consuming jobs were dealing with the loose straw after threshing and the cut hay. The labour shortages caused by the war, and the increased acreage that was being cultivated, made matters worse. The brothers realised that compacting the straw and hay into bales that could be more easily handled and stored would be extremely useful.

Glynne and David, along with George Williams, made their first baler for their own use by adapting existing machinery. The balers tightly packed the cut hay or straw into rectangular bales that could be efficiently transported and stacked in a barn. Local farmers were so impressed with the machine that they wanted their own and, in 1942, they began manufacture at the site of an old lead mine in Rhosesmor, making one machine at a time, using local farm lads as their work force.

Soldiers returning from the war, provided a large skilled work force and ex-army lathes, drills and other equipment were readily available. Demand for the balers was increasing and the business rapidly expanded, moving to a purpose built factory in Mold in 1958.

Other companies were also developing balers and farm machinery, especially in America, but the Jones machines were more successful locally as they were designed with the narrow lanes and gateways of North Wales in mind, and all the testing was done on local farms. They soon became equally popular in other parts of Britain with similar conditions.

Below: *Baler images*
(courtesy of Noel Jones)

Jones Balers at Mold Station en route for Australia! (courtesy of Noel Jones)

As the company grew, the range of products expanded and Jones Balers were exported across the world. The American company, Allis Chalmers ordered large numbers and eventually bought the whole company in 1961. The machines were then made in Wales and America for some years.

The next development that transformed harvesting was the introduction of the combine harvester that brought together harvesting and threshing into a single operation. The first combines were developed in America in the 19th century but they were large and cumbersome and it was not until the 1920s and 30s that smaller combines, more suited to British farms, were developed. They were not widely used in North Wales until much later, due to their high cost and unsuitability for the local conditions. The combine enabled the whole harvesting process to be done in the field in one operation.

The first combine harvester made by Jones Balers being tested at Penbedw, Nannerch, in the 1950s
(courtesy of Noel Jones)

Above left: *Combining at Ty Gwyn, early 1950s*

Above right: *Combining in Cheshire, about 2000*
(courtesy of Bernard Stanyer)

Below: *Combining in Gellifor, 1965*
(courtesy of Anne Williams)

Silaging at Ty Mawr, Tremeirchion, 2008 (courtesy of Mark Roberts)

Silaging

Silage, fermented grass, is a less weather dependent alternative to hay that provides a nutritious winter-feed for cattle. Hay needs several days of good weather to dry out properly and damp hay can rot and become worthless. Silage doesn't need to dry and is just left to wilt for one day before being baled and wrapped, or chopped and packed into silage pits, prior to fermentation. Farmers can cut two or three silage crops from the same field each season so yields are higher too. Silage is now far more widely used than hay. The large, plastic-wrapped silage bales and big silage pits covered in polythene and weighted down with tyres are familiar sights on farms nowadays, along with the distinctive sharp, sweet smell of silage.

Pottinger forager collecting silage, Maes-y-Groes Bella, Cilcain

After the war, farming continued to intensify and grants encouraged farmers to further increase food production. The improved machinery that was available enabled much steeper slopes to be cultivated and large areas of rough grassland and moorland on the lower slopes of the Clwydian Range were ploughed and reseeded.

Farm machinery has continued to develop rapidly. Anyone who was farming a century ago would be astounded by the size and power of the modern machines. Most tractors are over 100 horse power and many are far more powerful, hay tedders turn several swathes of hay at once and some ploughs can plough 10 furrows at a time. Electronics specialists are required to service the modern equipment, plugging in laptop computers to diagnose the faults! Some of the most modern tractors and harvesters have GPS and autosteering that programme the machine to drive in straight lines with the optimum distance between rows. With these machines, straight rows are the result of satellite navigation, rather than the skill of the ploughman! The days when harvesting and haymaking needed many hands are gone forever.

Large hay tedder working near Loggerheads

Baling hay, Ty'n-y-Caeau, Cilcain

Chapter 5

Tending the flocks

The upper slopes of the Clwydian Range, a mosaic of heather moorland, bilberry and rough grassland, have always been used for grazing. Sheep are the main grazing animal, although hardy cattle breeds would also have grazed the hillsides in earlier times. The most common sheep breed is the Welsh Mountain that is ideally suited to the moorland conditions. Their short, thick wool helps them to resist the heavy rain and bitter weather on the high ground and they are able to survive on very poor pasture.

Much of the moorland is common land. Graziers who live on the farms that border the open mountain have commoners rights to graze a certain number of animals on the moorland. It is important to graze at the correct level to keep both the moorland and the sheep in good condition. The sheep are usually put out on the hills in the winter to rest the lower land before lambing and again in the summer to enable the grass on the lower land to be cut for hay or silage. They have a natural territorial instinct, known as 'cynefin', whereby each group of sheep have their own section of hillside and generally stick to it. Each year the new lambs go with their mothers onto the hills and pick up the territorial instinct from their mothers.

'Our shepherd, Robert Thomas Jones, knew more about sheep than anyone. He could read the weather and would bring the sheep down from the mountain if he anticipated heavy snow but knew that rain didn't bother them.'

Captain Archdale, Penbedw, Nannerch

Left: *Sheep grazing near Graigfechan*
Right: *Lambs in snow*
(courtesy of Pete Lewis)

The area is known for its prize-winning sheep-breeders. Five generations of the Lloyd family from Sychdyn and Cildaugoed, Tremeirchion, have produced champion Welsh Mountain sheep that have won local, national and international shows. Richard Lloyd passed on his farming expertise to Martin Sivill, whose family lived next door to one of Richard's fields. Martin has continued to successfully show sheep and cattle, now breeding prizewinning Hampshire Down sheep at Glanrafon Farm, Waen.

Captain Archdale, from Penbedw, crossed Border Leicester rams with Welsh Mountain ewes to produce a larger ewe that combined the qualities of both sheep. The resulting cross, the Welsh Halfbred, has become a well-established breed that is popular across lowland England and Wales.

THE WELSH HALFBRED

*The mountain sheep are sweeter
But the valley sheep are fatter
So we married all the virtues
Of the former to the latter*

With Welsh Halfbred apologies to Thomas Love Peacock

'From the age of seven, I used to spend as long as I could out in the fields with Richard, watching him work and helping him. Richard taught me everything about farming, including how to breed and show livestock. He explained that winning at a big show was like a 'shop window' as it was such good advertising for the stock and they always sold well afterwards.'

Martin Sivill

Left: *Richard Lloyd winning the Royal Welsh Show*
(courtesy of Richard Lloyd)

Right: *Richard Lloyd and Martin Sivill and their prize-winning sheep with Princess Anne at the Royal Welsh Show, 1991.*
(courtesy of Martin Sivill)

Below: *Martin winning Young Handler at the Royal Welsh in 2001*
(courtesy of Martin Sivill)

Will Goodwin, Pantymwyn
(courtesy of Mona Williams)

Glyn working with Ben, one of his prize-winning sheepdogs
(courtesy of Glyn Jones)

'When I was 19, I accompanied my father and his friends to the sheepdog trials at Penbedw. They had been 'on the pop' all day and, by the time it was our turn, they were too inebriated to compete so I 'ran the dogs' instead and won! It was a wonderful feeling and I was hooked on trialling after that.'

Glyn Jones, Bwlch Isaf Farm, Bodfari

'I enjoy being on the hills with a few sheep dogs. Gathering sheep with good dogs is most rewarding, seeing their obedience and being in the wide open spaces, away from your fellow man!'

Peter Rowley Williams, chairman of the Moel Famau graziers

The Clwydian Range has produced several champion sheep-dog handlers, most notably Glyn Jones, international Supreme Champion Trialist and three times winner of the One Man and His Dog Trials. One of the oldest local events is the annual Rhes-y-cae sheepdog trials that has been running for over 60 years, and the Welsh National Trials were held at Penbedw in 2006.

The number of working sheepdogs is declining as sheep are now often gathered using quad bikes. Some farms use both bikes and sheepdogs but others no longer use dogs. There is a risk that the skills of sheepdog handling may die out unless young shepherds are prepared to take the time to train dogs.

'Our neighbour used to help us gather the sheep down from the hillside on his pony. Their help was invaluable as the pony could get to places that a quad bike couldn't.'

Phil Rundle, Bwlch Isaf Farm, Bodfari

Gathering *sheep on the Penbedw estate*
Left: *Penbedw, 1980*

Below: *Captain Archdale with Jock*
(courtesy of Captain Archdale)

Bottom: *The Garth, 2011*
(courtesy of Jackie Lewis)

'A good dog is invaluable – it gets to know what you're thinking, almost like telepathy. Quad bikes are useful but sheepdogs will always remain the best way to gather the sheep.'

Captain Archdale, Penbedw

Traditionally the heather is cut or burned on rotation to ensure that there is always a fresh growth of young shoots for the sheep. This management is also good for wildlife as it gives a mixed age of heather, ideal for the increasingly rare black and red grouse, who can find cover amongst the woody heather and fresh food from the young growth. Bracken is becoming a great problem, spreading across the hillsides and suppressing the growth of other plants. This is a recent problem as, in the past, it was cut for bedding and more cattle grazed the hillsides, trampling the young bracken.

In the early 1950s, Ken and Geoff Lewis pioneered bracken bruising using a tractor with caterpillar tracks. Bracken is still crushed or cut today but the steeper slopes can now be carefully sprayed from a helicopter.

'In the early 50s, I went on work experience to the Ministry of Agriculture to learn about machinery. Bracken crushing was one of my jobs on a Fordson County Crawler with a Holt bracken breaker. We worked on both sides of the Clwydian Range, often on very steep slopes. By chance a vet from Mold, Stanley Jones, was coming to see a sick cow on our farm and had seen me working on a slope below the Clwyd Gate. He mentioned that he had seen some fool driving a tractor down the steep slope and when my father said it was me, he exclaimed, "You want to get the silly bugger from there – he's going to kill himself!" - I was mad in those days!'

Gwyndaf Davies

Left: *Crushing bracken on the Clwydian Range overlooking Ruthin, 1955,*
(courtesy of Gwyndaf Davies)

Above: *Gwyndaf Davies*

Right: *Red grouse in heather*
(courtesy of the Clwydian Range AONB)

Glynne Roberts bottle feeding, Henblas, Tremerichion
(courtesy of the Roberts family)

Weak lambs being warmed by the stove
(courtesy of Ken Lewis)

Pregnant ewes in the lambing shed, Maes Alyn, Cilcain

Lambing

Lambing remains one of the busiest times for the farmer who has to regularly check on the heavily pregnant ewes and be on hand at all hours to assist with a difficult birth. Traditionally lambing took place in early spring, after the worst of the winter weather but nowadays, some lowland farmers prefer to lamb in January to have lambs ready for sale by Easter, when they can usually be sold for higher prices.

The sheep are brought down from higher land for lambing so that they are away from the worst of the weather and can be more carefully monitored. Some, especially the early lambs, are lambed indoors but many are born outdoors, often in sheltered fields close to the farm, and all mothers and young lambs are soon back out in the fields. Some lambs need extra help and all the family may get involved, bottle feeding or warming weak ones in the range or by the fire.

'Every year we get two or three orphan lambs. I put them in a box of hay by the fire to warm them up and give them a drink. Once they're on their feet, we move them to the shippon and I bottle feed them three times a day until they're ready to go out into the fields.'

Heather Lewis, Cyfnant Uchaf Farm, Llanarmon-yn-Iâl

(courtesy of Jackie Lewis)

Gaynor Roberts bottle feeding, Ty Mawr, Tremerichion
(courtesy of Mark Roberts)

Shearing

In early summer each sheep is sheared. Until the mid 20th century this was done by hand using shears. Neighbouring farms helped each other at shearing time, gathering the sheep from the hills and bringing them down to the farm, where several shearers would work on wooden benches or boards, with several more hands rolling and packing the fleeces.

'Each June we used to gather the mountain sheep for shearing at Cwm-Llydan, near Llanferres. I remember, in 1949, we hand sheared 240 sheep there! We sheared all day until 11pm – I was hot, sweaty and greasy by the end and was grateful for the hip flask of Irish whisky the farmer gave me!'

John James Parry, Maes y Garnedd, Tafarn-y-Gelyn

Shearing at Nercwys, possibly at Bryn Farm (courtesy of Ray Davies)

Shepherds Delight by Ken Lewis

At long last June is here
With weather fine and warm,
The sky above is blue and clear
No sign of rain or storm.

The ewes have gone back to the hill,
Each to her own retreat.
Free to graze where ere they will
Offspring at their feet.

The winter was long to feed those dams.
Cake bills there were many
But to see that lovely crop of lambs
It was worth every penny.

For a week or two we can relax
Before we start to clip
And pack the wool in those big sacks,
Then we'll have to dip.

Ken Lewis shearing at Cyfnant Uchaf
(courtesy of Ken Lewis)

The first shearing machines were not much faster than hand shearing and required someone to turn the handle to make them work. The electric clippers that replaced them enabled much faster shearing, coupled with the improved shearing techniques developed by New Zealander, Godfrey Bowen, who demonstrated and instructed across the world in the 1950s and 60s. Nowadays, most large flocks are shorn by professional shearing teams, often from New Zealand, who move from farm to farm. The rolled fleeces are packed into large sacks that are collected by and sold through the Wool Marketing Board.

A skilled hand-shearer could shear a sheep in ten minutes, whereas it is possible to shear in under a minute, using modern electric clippers. New Zealander Dave Fagan, who has been shearing at Penbedw for 28 years, has been world champion many times and his colleague, Dion King currently holds the world record for lamb-shearing of 866 lambs in 7 hours!

'When I first started shearing after the war, we sheared by hand on benches. In the 1950s, we bought electric shearing machines and I went to learn the new shearing techniques from New Zealander, Godfrey Bowen, who was demonstrating locally.'

Captain Archdale, Penbedw

Above: *Early machine shearing at College Farm, Trefnant*
(courtesy of Bernard Stanyer)

Left: *Shearing competition at the Young Farmers Club Rally, Penbedw, 1954, judged by Glynne Davies*
(courtesy of Gwyndaf Davies)

Sam Griffiths shearing at Cilcain (courtesy of Phil Parsons)

Wrapping and bagging fleeces at Maes Alyn and Llety, Cilcain Cilcain (top and bottom left photographs courtesy of Phil Parsons)

Sheep scab and other infections caused by parasites such as mites and ticks can be very serious. Traditionally sheep were dipped into a tank filled with insecticide. Nowadays parasites can also be controlled by injecting at the right time of year but properly done dipping is still the most effective way to control sheep scab.

'We dipped the sheep annually to protect against Sheep Scab. It was compulsory because it was a disease that spread so quickly and the local policeman had to be there to make sure it was all done properly. On my farm we didn't have a dipping tub, so we went to a neighbouring farm. The bath for dipping was just a trough dug in the earth, lined with bricks, 4 foot deep. One end had some steps. You'd hold the sheep by their front legs and gently drop them in the deep end and then they'd use the steps to get out on the other side.'

Idris Jones, Treuddyn

Chapter 6

Cattle and other livestock

Traditionally, hardy Welsh Black cattle would have been grazed on the moorland in the summer and would have been brought down to the lower pasture in the winter. These were the cattle walked in their thousands across the Welsh hills to English markets by the drovers and they continued to be the mainstay of Welsh farming into the early 20th century. They were a dual-purpose breed that could be milked but also produced good meat. Nowadays, a much wider variety of breeds are kept, specially bred for optimum milk production or high quality meat. Beef and dairy farming are now very different enterprises and only a small number of specialised dairy farms remain. Most cattle are now over-wintered indoors, fed on silage and concentrates, and are only put out to graze the lower pastures in summer.

Right: *Mrs Roberts, Pen Isa'r Wen, Tremeirchion* (courtesy of Kevin and Catherin Roberts)

Far right: *Milk churns, Nercwys* (courtesy of Ray Davies)

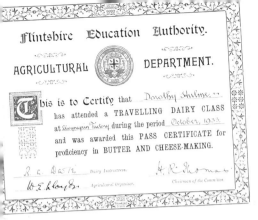

Until the later part of the 20th century, most farms kept milking cows, producing a few gallons of milk each day as well as cattle to fatten for meat.

'As children we would milk by hand on a 3 legged stool with a bucket by our knees. The milk would then be put through the separator – to separate the skim from the cream. The cream would then be turned into butter. In the 1940s we got a milking machine - I was so glad when we did as it was so much better than the stool and our hands!'

Idris Jones

Much of the milk was used to make cheese and butter. In 1907, Llweni Hall Dairy School was established, funded jointly by Denbighshire and Flintshire County Councils. Later, Llysfasi Agricultural College also ran dairy courses and the councils organized travelling dairy classes. Several small butter and cheese-making enterprises were set up. One of these was Nercwys Cheese Factory, set up in 1919 in a former colliery engine house. Local farmers brought their milk on horse and cart to the factory for cheese-making. The collected milk was warmed in vats and rennet added to separate it into curds and whey. Farmers bought the whey to feed to their livestock and the curds were put into wooden vats and compressed to form cheese. It ran successfully for over ten years, giving employment to local girls and a large sales outlet for the dairy farms.

Top left: _Cheese-making certificate (courtesy of Dorothy Jones)_

Left: _Nercwys Cheese factory (courtesy of Ray Davies)_

Nercwys Cheese factory (courtesy of Ray Davies)

Another was Llandrynog Creamery that was established in the 1920s to make butter and cream, but began cheese-making a few years later. It is still going strong today, now one of largest cheese producers in the UK and the largest milk-processing site in Wales. Its products include the award-winning Cadog Welsh Cheddar.

Until after the Second World War, much milk from Flintshire farms was sold to Liverpool dairies, often sent in churns by train to Liverpool. Many farms sold milk locally, running a daily milk-round, initially delivering their milk door to door by horse and cart. The milk was ladled from large cans into the jugs left by each householder. Later, electric milk floats or, in the rural areas, more robust vans and Landrovers, replaced the horse and carts. A few farms still run milk rounds but their numbers are decreasing due mainly to the availability of low priced milk in supermarkets.

Rhydymwyn farmer, Keith Davies, delivering milk in Cilcain from his organic dairy herd

Mount Pleasant Dairy Milk float, Gwernaffield, 1920s
(courtesy of the Shawcross family)

Wright dairy floats, Rhyd Farm, Dyserth. The dairy supplied customers in Rhyl during the 1940s
(courtesy of Pat Jones)

The Williams dairy farm at Greenbank, Tremeirchion won the CLA Best Kept Farm award in 1964

Below: *Cleaning the clusters on the milking machine* (courtesy of Gwynfa Derosa)

In 1933, the government established the Milk Marketing Board to control milk production, distribution and marketing (many will remember the slogan, 'Drinkapintamilkaday'). It was a great help to dairy farmers, ensuring that a fair price was paid and that there was consistency in pricing across the country.

Each farm put their fresh milk into 10 gallon metal churns. These were collected from the farm gate each day and replaced with empty churns. The Milk Marketing Board arranged for the sale and distribution of the milk – some was bottled for sale, some sent for butter, yoghurt or cheese making, some for dried

Milking demonstration to Colomendy pupils at Cae'r Odyn Farm, Tafarn-y-Gelyn
(courtesy of the Jones family)

Glynne Roberts feeding a calf, Henblas, Tremeirchion
(courtesy of the Roberts family)

and other milk products, and some sent to companies such as Cadburys for making chocolate. The weekly milk cheque was really important to many farmers, as money from sheep and other livestock only came when they had been sold so milk money was often their only regular income.

Large numbers of farms have gone out of dairying over the past 20 years, partly due to the introduction of European Union milk quotas, the dissolution of the Milk Marketing Board, the big drop in milk prices in 2000 and the large investment in new technology needed to run an efficient modern milking parlour.

The milking process has changed beyond recognition since the days of hand milking. It takes about ten minutes to milk a cow by hand, depending on the temperament of the cow and the skill of the milker. A milking machine takes about 5 minutes per cow but, in a large parlour, many cows can be milked at once. Modern parlours have computer systems analyzing the milk yield of each cow, calculating her optimum food requirements and delivering the right amount of food to her.

'When I was a boy there were about 40 farms that had dairy cows around Cilcain. I'm the only one left now but our dairy herd has grown from 40 cows in 1968 to around 240 now. I remember when we got our first milking machines in the 1940s and built our first milk parlour in 1968. In our modern parlour, we can milk over 200 cows in about 90 minutes and the whole system is regulated by computer. Each cow wears a transponder round her neck that is read automatically by computer when she enters the milking parlour!'

Harry Williams, Fforest Farm, Cilcain

Fforest Farm, Cilcain

Beef is produced from both herds bred specifically for meat production and from dairy herds. Some farms breed beef calves, known as 'sucklers' because they suckle milk from their mothers for 6-9months. After this they are fattened or 'finished' for slaughter, either on grass outdoors, or more intensively indoors, and killed around 2 years old. Dairy bull calves, and cross-bred dairy heifers are also fattened and sold for meat. These calves only suckle for a few days as their mothers are needed for milking. They are fed on artificial milk and then finished in the same way as the other calves. Many local farmers don't breed themselves but buy calves to 'finish' prior to selling for slaughter.

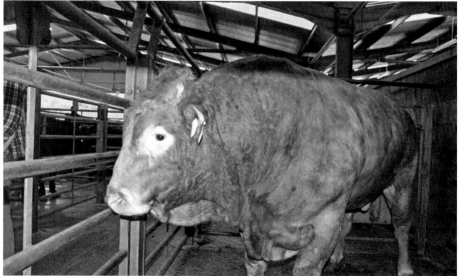

Gwen Wright, Rhyd Farm, Dyserth with her triplet calves - multiple births are unusual for cattle so these triplets were very special!
(courtesy of Pat Jones)

Left: *Pistyll Farm Bodfari* (courtesy of Fiona Evans)

Below right: *Moving geese, Nercwys* (courtesy of Ray Davies)

Below left: *Sow with piglets, Rhesgoed Farm, Llanbedr DC* (courtesy of Rhesgoed Farm)

In the past, most farms also kept a couple of sows that were fed on scraps and a mixed flock of ducks and hens that wandered freely around the farm. The sale of eggs often provided a bit of extra money for the farmer's wife. The numbers of free-range poultry flocks reduced during the 1950s and 60s when intensive battery farming of poultry became widespread. In the same period intensive indoor piggeries replaced the more natural pig-rearing system. A few Clwydian farms still keep free range hens and rear traditional breeds of pigs outdoors.

'I remember taking the sow to the boar in Llandyrnog in our Austin 7 van. We had to shove her in the back and close the door quickly. All the way there she'd have her nose on the passenger's shoulder!'

Glyn Jones, Bwlch Isaf Farm, Bodfari

'When I was a girl we kept a pig on the farm and towards the end of the year we'd kill the pig to have meat over the winter. Mam saved the blood to make black pudding then, with Dad's help, she'd cut the pig into bits and put salt into the meat to preserve it. When it was ready we hung it from the beams on the ceiling. It was quite exciting when the pig was killed and seeing it hanging there. It was part of life when you had animals on a farm and I looked forward to eating the bacon - a lot of fat but very tasty!'

Anne Woodward, Tafarn-y-gelyn

Jeannie and John M. Roberts feeding pigs and poultry, Ty'n Celyn, Llanbedr (courtesy of John Roberts)

Cecil and Evelyn Roberts feeding turkeys at Pen Isa'r Waen, Tremeirchion (courtesy of Kevin and Catherin Roberts)

Chapter 7

Buying and selling

Regular livestock fairs have been at the hub of farming since Medieval times, drawing buyers and sellers from far and wide. Ruthin, Denbigh and Mold all developed as market towns around their central market squares.

The livestock market continues to be a key part of farming locally with regular markets held at Ruthin, Mold and St Asaph. Formerly there were also markets at Denbigh and Abergele. The auction continues to be far more than just a place to buy and sell. It is a social occasion, gives farmers a chance to meet and catch up with fellow farmers, as they weigh up the current prices and carefully assess the beasts up for sale.

'Up until we got a wagon in the 1950s, we used to walk the sheep along the road from Treuddyn to market in Mold, using sheepdogs to keep the flock together.'

Idris Jones

Left: *Mold Livestock Market, 2011*

Top: *Huw Edwards, Highgate, winning Champion Butcher's Beast, 1982*
(courtesy of Ruthin Farmers Auction Company)

Right: *Ruthin Farmers Auction, 2011*

Bottom right: *Walking sheep along the A494 at Loggerheads*
(courtesy of the Clwydian Range AONB)

Mold livestock market is still in the middle of the town

Prizewinner at Mold auction, 1947 (courtesy of Elvet Pierce)

Loading sheep after the sale

Mold livestock market is still in the town centre and has been on the same site for over 100 years. It holds auctions every Monday and Friday and is now the biggest cattle auction in North Wales.

'We had to start very early in the morning to walk our animals to market and by the time we had penned them up we were thirsty and hungry so the cafes in town were very busy and had a good atmosphere. It was and still is important for farmers to have a place to meet up and socialize – everyone was in good humour at the market, as it was pay day for them.'

Clwyd Hughes, Llangwyfan Farm, talking about Denbigh market

Once farms began to aquire lorries, landrovers and trailers, animals could be easily moved longer distances, and the need for several markets relatively close together diminished. The number of markets peaked after the Second World War but has steadily declined since then. However, those that remain have become larger and are still thriving. The change to motorized transport also enabled the farmers' wives to accompany their husbands to town on market days, shopping in the town while the men were at the auction.

'Both husband and wife used to get dressed up in their best clothes to travel into town for market days, the streets would be very quiet other days of the week.'

Clwyd Hughes, Llangwyfan Farm

'I worked at the top auction at Ruthin three days a week for some extra income. After the auction, we had to walk the stock that had been sold for meat up to the slaughterhouse at Crown House.'

Glyn Jones, Bwlch Isaf Farm, Bodfari

Below: *Small slaughter house, Mwrog Street, Ruthin, circa 1910s (courtesy of John Jones & son, Ruthin)*

Paul Williams assessing the lambs at Mold market

Prize winning bullock from the Ruthin Winter Fatstock sale
(courtesy of John Jones & son, Ruthin)

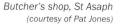

Butcher's shop, St Asaph
(courtesy of Pat Jones)

Traditionally local butchers came to the market each week to buy the animals that they felt would provide the best meat. Nowadays, most of the meat is sold directly to wholesalers and much is exported but some local butchers are still regulars at the markets, carefully choosing the best lambs and cattle. There is still great competition to purchase the prizewinning animals at the Christmas fatstock sales.

'I first came to Mold market with my Dad when I was 14 years old and he taught me how to choose the best animals for butchering. At that time there were 8 butchers in Mold but I'm the only one left. I have been coming here twice a week for 40 years.'

Paul Williams, Mold butcher

The original market on the square in Ruthin
(courtesy of Ruthin Farmers Auction Company)

Ruthin market was originally held on St Peter's Square in the middle of the town. In 1905, in order to stop the streets being congested with livestock it moved to rented land at the bottom of the hill, becoming known as 'ocsiwn Isaf" or the lower market. A second market was later established 50 yards higher up, becoming known as 'ocsiwn uchaf', the higher market. The two companies were combined 1921 to form Ruthin Farmers Auction Company, with shares bought by local farmers.

By the 1980s, trade at the auctions had increased greatly and caused considerable congestion in the town on market days. Eventually, in 1992, the market was relocated to a purpose-built site on the Denbigh Road on edge of the town. Denbigh market closed soon afterwards. The offices of Ruthin Farmers Auction are still on the site of the old upper auction. Regular auctions for cattle and sheep are held three days per week, plus a monthly pig sale and occasional special sales of machinery, ponies and sheepdogs.

Winter fatstock sale at Ruthin, 1978
(courtesy of Ruthin Farmers Auction Company)

Above: *Spectators at the Christmas Fatstock sale, the higher market, 'ocsiwn uchaf' Ruthin, around 1950*
(courtesy of Ruthin Farmers Auction Company)

Right: *Images of Ruthin Farmers Auction, 2011 (courtesy of Jo Danson and Lorna Jenner)*

Chapter 8

Looking forward

The numbers employed on farms in the Clwydian Range have decreased considerably in the past 100 years. Many youngsters are turning away from farming as the income generated from the average family farm is insufficient to be able to pay them a reasonable wage and they have much wider career options than their grandparents had. There are undoubtedly more lucrative and easier ways of earning a living! The average age of farmers is rising and the proportion of farmers under 35 halved between 1990 and 2005. Farm incomes have dropped by more than 50% since 1995 and farming faces serious difficulties. Many traditional farm buildings have become redundant with the reduced labour force and changing farming practices. A few have been converted to dwellings or for alternative businesses, but many are derelict.

However, not all youngsters are deterred and there are still many farms in the Clwydian Range that have been run by the same family for generations. The Young Farmers Club still flourishes in and around the Clwydian Range with active groups in Cilcain, Treuddyn, Northop and Whitford. Many of these younger farmers are part-time, working on other jobs such as agricultural contracting to supplement the low farming incomes.

Many farms have diversified using the redundant buildings to provide livery for horses, winter storage for caravans or to store marquees. Several farms have developed some of their land as caravan parks or offer bed and breakfast. Many farmers are signing up to Conservation Schemes where they are paid a premium to manage their land to enhance the biodiversity. Some sell their products directly from the farm, such as free-range eggs, Christmas turkeys or pick your own fruit in season. Rhesgoed Farm at Llanbedr DC opened a farm shop in 2005 and won 'The Best Achiever in Agriculture' award from the NFU in 2006. All their meat is from the Clwydian Range, mainly their own animals but supplemented by meat sourced from other local farms. In addition they stock a range of other locally sourced foods.

In parallel with the increased mechanization of farming, there seems to be a real nostalgia for the old ways with historic farming programmes drawing large audiences and ploughing matches and vintage rallies well supported. The Vintage Machinery Society is flourishing, old tractors are prized possessions and old steam engines can cost many thousands of pounds.

Left: *Gathering sheep at the Garth, Cilcain*

Left: *The youngest farmer at Ruthin auction, Osian Gruffydd, Nant Ucha, Pentrecelyn, selling his pet lambs*

Above: *Sioned Williams working at the family farm shop, Rhesgoed Farm, Llanbedr DC*
Right: *Dairy Farmer, Gareth Williams, Fforest Farm, Cilcain*

Above: *Budding sheep breeders from Bryn Farm, Tremeirchion at the Caerwys Show, around 2005 (courtesy of Delyth Potts)*

Right: *Fron Farm Caravan and Camping Park, Hendre*

Below: *Contractors baling at Ty'n-y-Caeau, Cilcain*

The changes in farming in the past century have been enormous. Modern farming involves less back-breaking manual labour as it has become more mechanized, but not all the changes have been positive and there will be more challenges to face in the coming years. However, farmers remain the custodians of our countryside and will continue to play a vital role in conserving the landscape of the Clwydian Range. Whatever their age, they are still country folk above all, knowledgeable about the wildlife, tuned in to the weather, enjoying the changing seasons and the outdoor life.

This poem, by 93 year old Ken Lewis, reflects this lasting bond between farmer and the land.

Seasonal Contentment

Summer, autumn, winter, spring,
We see them come and go.
Without fail they always bring
Sun, rain, gales, frost and snow.

As I walk on the Clywdian Range
On my shepherd's rounds,
I always enjoy each season's change
And the various wildlife sounds.

Enjoy the sound of the curlew's call,
The rushing water as the stream we pass.
The silence as the snowflakes fall
And the grouse when away they dash.

When I look across Snowdonia's peaks
Or down the vale to the open sea,
Across to the east where industry speaks
Or Merioneth, it fascinates me.

No matter what the season,
Be the weather foul or fair
I always find a reason
For contentment when I'm there.

Ken Lewis, Cyfnant Uchaf Farm, Llanarmon-yn-Iâl

Harry Williams in a ploughing match on his Fordson tractor
(courtesy of Harry Williams)